bowmar

autumn

written by Lucille Wood
designed and illustrated by Paul Taylor

RHYTHMS TO READING

Book and Record Sets
A Multi-Sensory Approach to Music and Reading

A companion recording is available for this book and all others in the RHYTHMS TO READING series. Each picture in this book represents an action song or a descriptive musical composition which is included with narration on the long-playing record.

Reading the simple text under each picture continues the unique multi-sensory experience for the young child that begins with his active, happy response to the stories and music of the recording. This simple text is included on the recording for use in the classroom and at the listening post.

On the left-hand page, beginning on page 4, are printed the full story and song lyrics heard on the recording. This page is for the use of teachers, parents, and children who are experienced readers.

Repetition is essential to learning. Learning which might otherwise be derived from tedious drill is here developed in an enjoyable, esthetic context.

Research indicates that children learn to read more quickly and easily words that are related to large muscle activity, esthetic experience and tongue-tickling rhymes.

When reading experiences are introduced through music, song and vigorous movement

- *memory is reinforced and tensions released, creating an atmosphere that encourages learning.*

- *the flow of language comes more naturally, encouraging the child to read in complete sentences.*

- *the number of clues which aid the child in reading are multiplied.*

- *word meanings are clarified and sight vocabulary is developed automatically.*

First Printing . . . . October 1970
Second Printing . . . . March 1972

What do we do on an autumn day?

What do you think we might do
on a sunny autumn day?
Let's take a friend's hand
and walk through the dry leaves
that cover the ground.
Listen to the rustle and crackle of the leaves
as we walk on this crisp autumn day.

We walk with a friend through the autumn leaves.

Let's rake the leaves into a big pile.

Rake the leaves and rake the leaves
And rake them in a pile;
Rake the leaves and rake the leaves,
Then stop and rest awhile.

We rake the leaves, yellow, red and brown.

Now we have a big, crackly pile of leaves.

(1) One by one, we jump in the leaves;
   One by one, we jump in the leaves,
   One by one, we jump in the leaves,
   And all fall down together.

(2) Oh what fun to jump in the leaves, etc.

   (Repeat)

The leaves are beautiful colors
of yellow, red and brown.
Pick up some leaves to take home.

(1) Pick up a leaf and put it in a basket,
   Pick up a leaf and put it in a basket,
   Pick up a leaf and put it in a basket,
   Yellow, red and brown.

(2) I found a leaf to put in my basket, etc.

(3) How many leaves do you have in your basket? etc.
   One, two, three, four, five.

8

We jump in the leaves and all fall down.

Look!
The fallen leaves are playing "Follow the Leader."
The wind tells them what to do.
They run and skip or jump
and leap through the air.
Sometimes they move very slowly.
Let's play "Follow the Leader" like the leaves.
How would it feel to be as light as a leaf
blown by the autumn wind?

We leap and run and skip like the leaves in the autumn wind.

We are birds that fly south to a warm country
when the cold autumn winds blow.
Get ready to fly away over the houses
and over the trees.

They flap their wings and fly away,
They fly and fly and fly all day,
Fly, fly, fly.   Fly, fly, fly.
(Repeat)

They hop on the ground looking for something to eat.

They find a bug on the cold, bare ground,
They chirp and chirp and hop around,
Hop, hop, hop.   Hop, hop, hop.
(Repeat)

Up into the sky they fly again
over the rivers and mountains.

They flap their wings and fly away,
They fly and fly and fly all day,
Fly, fly, fly.   Fly, fly, fly.
(Repeat)

12

We fly like birds over the rivers and hills.

When evening comes they fly to a tree
where the little birds play a game.
Let's play like the birds.

The first little bird flies around and around,
The second little bird flies down to the ground.

The third little bird stretches his wings,
The fourth little bird just sits and sings.

The fifth little bird flies to a nest,
The sixth little bird wants to rest.

The seventh little bird says, "Peep, peep, peep."
All the little birds fall fast asleep.

We play like birds and find a tree.

We are tall trees in the autumn wind.

Back and forth and back and forth,
See your branches sway;
Back and forth and back and forth,
On a windy autumn day.

Who has seen the wind?
Neither I nor you;
But when the leaves hang trembling,
The wind is passing through.

Who has seen the wind?
Neither you nor I;
But when the trees bow down their heads,
The wind is passing by.

(By Christina Georgiana Rossetti)

We sway like tall trees in the autumn wind.

We are leaves
that twirl and whirl down from the trees
and go to sleep on the ground.

Blow, wind, blow,
Blow, wind, blow.
Whirling and twirling and spinning around,
Little red leaves fall down to the ground.
Sleep, little leaves,
Sleep, little leaves.

Blow, wind, blow,
Blow, wind, blow.
Whirling and twirling and spinning around,
Little brown leaves fall down to the ground.
Sleep, little leaves,
Sleep, little leaves.

We whirl to the ground like autumn leaves.

We pick apples and put them in a basket.

Climbing up an apple tree,
Climbing up an apple tree,
Climbing up an apple tree,
To pick red apples, one, two, three.

Pick one apple, red and round,
Pick one apple, red and round,
Pick one apple, red and round,
Then jump and jump down to the ground.

We pick red apples, one, two, three, four, five.

We lift pumpkins from the ground
and put them in a wagon.

Walking through a pumpkin patch,
Walking through a pumpkin patch,
Find the pumpkins ripe and round,
Orange pumpkins on the ground.

Lift a pumpkin from the ground,
Lift it to the wagon;
Lift a pumpkin from the ground,
Heavy pumpkins, orange and round.

22

We lift orange pumpkins and put them in a wagon.

Long ago, children danced play-party games
at the harvest parties.
We stand in a circle and dance "Old Brass Wagon."

(1) Clap your hands, the old brass wagon,
Clap your hands, the old brass wagon,
Clap your hands, the old brass wagon,
You're the one, my darling.

(2) Circle to the left, the old brass wagon, etc.

(3) Circle to the right, the old brass wagon, etc.

(4) Turn around, the old brass wagon, etc.

We dance "Old Brass Wagon."

We remember the first Thanksgiving Day
and sing about Indians and Pilgrims.
The boys may be the Indians.

One little, two little, three little Indians,
Four little, five little, six little Indians,
Seven little, eight little, nine little Indians,
Ten little Indian boys.

Ten little, nine little, eight little Indians,
Seven little, six little, five little Indians,
Four little, three little, two little Indians,
One little Indian boy.

We sing about Indians.

The girls may be the Pilgrims.

One little, two little, three little Pilgrims,
Four little, five little, six little Pilgrims,
Seven little, eight little, nine little Pilgrims,
Ten little Pilgrim girls.

Ten little, nine little, eight little Pilgrims,
Seven little, six little, five little Pilgrims,
Four little, three little, two little Pilgrims,
One little Pilgrim girl.

We sing about Pilgrims.

We sing a song of Thanksgiving.

Two little children on Thanksgiving Day
Bow their heads and quietly pray:
"I thank Thee, God, for father and mother,
Teach us to love and help each other;
I thank Thee, God, for Thy loving care,
Teach us to give and how to share."
Two little children on Thanksgiving Day
Bow their heads and quietly pray.

("Thanksgiving Prayer" reprinted and recorded by
permission from SINGING-FUN by Lucille F. Wood
and Louise Binder Scott. Copyright 1954 by
McGraw-Hill, Inc.)

We sing a song of Thanksgiving.

the end